Fractions and Decimals

5–6

Written by
Vicky Shiotsu

Editors: Carla Hamaguchi and Jennifer Busby
Illustrator: Corbin Hillam
Production: Carrie Rickmond
Cover Designer: Barbara Peterson
Art Director: Moonhee Pak
Project Manager: Collene Dobelmann
Project Director: Betsy Morris

Table of Contents

Introduction

Fractions and Decimals 5–6 contains ready-to-use activity pages to provide your students with skill practice. The activities can be used to supplement and enhance what your students are already learning at school. Give an activity page to students as independent class work, or send the pages home as homework to reinforce skills taught in class. An answer key is included at the end of the book for verification of student responses.

This book provides activities that will directly assist students in practicing basic skills and concepts. The structure of the book enhances students' learning and enables them to meet new challenges with confidence. The book is divided into two sections: the first section features fractions; the second presents decimals. The activity pages in the book introduce skills in an orderly progression to ensure students' success. Many of the pages also provide problem-solving activities that allow students to apply what they have learned and to practice critical-thinking skills. In addition, review pages at the end of each section let you evaluate students' learning.

Students will receive reinforcement in the following skills:

- Comparing fractions
- Adding and subtracting fractions
- Adding and subtracting mixed numbers
- Multiplying and dividing fractions
- Finding the least common denominator
- Comparing decimals
- Rounding decimals
- Adding and subtracting decimals
- Multiplying and dividing decimals
- Converting fractions to decimals

Use Fractions and Decimals 5–6 to reinforce or extend concepts and skills. "Recharge" skill review with the ready-to-go activities in this book, and give students the power to succeed!

Identifying Fractional Parts

$$\frac{3}{5}$$

The numerator tells how many parts of a whole you are looking at.

The denominator tells how many parts there are altogether.

Write a fraction that tells what part is shaded.

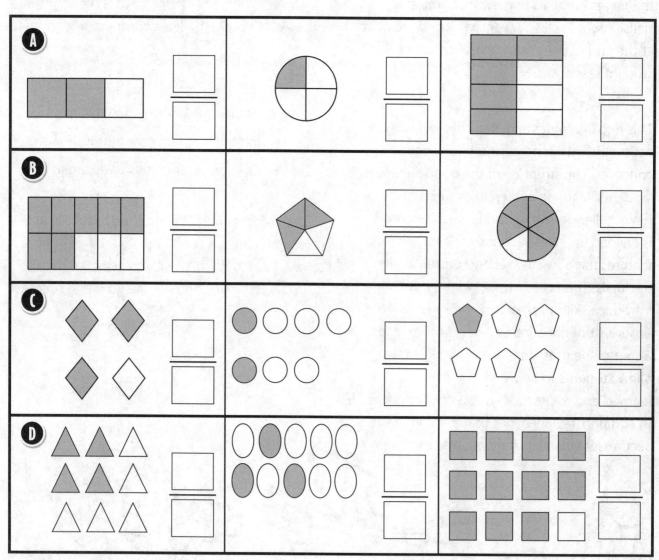

Find the fractions.

E There are 12 paper squares. If 7 of the squares are red, what fraction of the squares is not red?

_____

F There are 15 flowers. If 4 of the flowers are pink and 4 of them are white, what fraction of the flowers is pink or white?

_____

Name _____ Date _____

Equivalent Fractions

Fractions that have the same value are equivalent fractions. You can multiply or divide to find equivalent fractions.

$$\frac{1 \times 2}{2 \times 2} = \frac{2}{4}$$

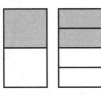

$$\frac{1}{2} = \frac{2}{4}$$

$$\frac{6 \div 3}{9 \div 3} = \frac{2}{3}$$

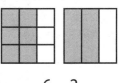

$$\frac{6}{9} = \frac{2}{3}$$

Multiply to find equivalent fractions.

A $\frac{1}{2} = \frac{}{8}$ $\frac{1}{4} = \frac{}{12}$ $\frac{1}{3} = \frac{}{9}$ $\frac{1}{5} = \frac{}{10}$

B $\frac{2}{3} = \frac{}{12}$ $\frac{3}{4} = \frac{}{8}$ $\frac{5}{6} = \frac{}{12}$ $\frac{7}{9} = \frac{}{18}$

Divide to find equivalent fractions.

C $\frac{8}{10} = \frac{}{5}$ $\frac{9}{12} = \frac{}{4}$ $\frac{2}{6} = \frac{}{3}$ $\frac{4}{10} = \frac{}{5}$

D $\frac{4}{16} = \frac{}{4}$ $\frac{20}{24} = \frac{}{6}$ $\frac{16}{20} = \frac{}{5}$ $\frac{15}{18} = \frac{}{6}$

Write equivalent fractions.

E $\frac{6}{36} = \frac{}{12}$ $\frac{4}{9} = \frac{}{18}$ $\frac{3}{8} = \frac{}{24}$ $\frac{5}{15} = \frac{}{3}$

F $\frac{4}{12} = \frac{}{3}$ $\frac{7}{10} = \frac{}{20}$ $\frac{3}{5} = \frac{}{15}$ $\frac{6}{30} = \frac{}{5}$

G $\frac{6}{10} = \frac{}{5}$ $\frac{18}{24} = \frac{}{4}$ $\frac{7}{12} = \frac{}{36}$ $\frac{10}{15} = \frac{}{3}$

Simplest Form

A fraction is in the simplest form when 1 is the greatest number that can divide the numerator and denominator evenly. To simplify a fraction, keep dividing the numerator and denominator by a common factor until you can't divide anymore.

$$\frac{12}{18} \rightarrow \frac{12 \div 2}{18 \div 2} = \frac{6}{9} \rightarrow \frac{6 \div 3}{9 \div 3} = \frac{2}{3}$$

The simplest form of ¹²⁄₁₈ is ⅔.

Write each fraction in simplest form.

A $\frac{6}{8} =$ $\frac{4}{6} =$ $\frac{5}{10} =$ $\frac{12}{15} =$

B $\frac{6}{21} =$ $\frac{5}{20} =$ $\frac{16}{24} =$ $\frac{3}{27} =$

C $\frac{9}{15} =$ $\frac{8}{12} =$ $\frac{15}{18} =$ $\frac{28}{35} =$

D $\frac{16}{28} =$ $\frac{21}{27} =$ $\frac{9}{30} =$ $\frac{15}{24} =$

Solve. Write the answers in simplest form.

E   There are 21 flowers. If 9 of the flowers are yellow, what fraction of the flowers is yellow?

_____

F   Mrs. Blair's class has 30 students. If 3 of the students are absent today, what fraction of the class is in school?

_____

G   There are 35 balloons. If 21 of the balloons are blue, what fraction of the balloons is not blue?

_____

H   Matt had $40. He spent $10 on books and $14 on markers. What fraction of his money did he spend?

_____

Fractions and Decimals • 5–6 © 2007 Creative Teaching Press

Name _____ Date _____

Comparing Fractions—Like Denominators, Like Numerators

When comparing fractions that have the same denominators, look at the numerators. The fraction with the larger numerator is greater.

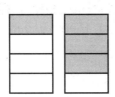

$$\frac{1}{4} < \frac{3}{4}$$

When comparing fractions that have the same numerators, look at the denominators. The fraction with the smaller denominator is greater.

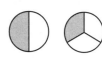

$$\frac{1}{2} > \frac{1}{3}$$

Compare the fractions. Write > or < in the circles.

A $\frac{1}{2} \bigcirc \frac{1}{3}$ $\frac{4}{5} \bigcirc \frac{2}{5}$ $\frac{2}{3} \bigcirc \frac{1}{3}$ $\frac{4}{7} \bigcirc \frac{6}{7}$

B $\frac{1}{8} \bigcirc \frac{1}{5}$ $\frac{3}{7} \bigcirc \frac{3}{4}$ $\frac{5}{6} \bigcirc \frac{5}{10}$ $\frac{2}{5} \bigcirc \frac{2}{9}$

Write the fractions in order from the least to the greatest.

C $\frac{1}{7}, \frac{1}{4}, \frac{1}{9}, \frac{1}{3}$ **D** $\frac{3}{8}, \frac{7}{8}, \frac{5}{8}, \frac{2}{8}$ **E** $\frac{5}{6}, \frac{5}{10}, \frac{5}{12}, \frac{5}{9}$

_____   _____   _____

Solve.

F Lisa, Jamie, and Sandy each made a bracelet with 24 beads. On Lisa's bracelet, $\frac{2}{12}$ of the beads were blue. On Jamie's bracelet, $\frac{2}{6}$ of the beads were blue. On Sandy's bracelet, $\frac{2}{8}$ of the beads were blue.

Who used the greatest number of blue beads? _____

Who used the fewest number of blue beads? _____

Name ______________________________ Date ____________

Comparing Fractions by Finding Common Denominators

When comparing fractions that have different denominators, first find equivalent fractions that have a common denominator. Then compare.

Example: Compare $\frac{2}{5}$ and $\frac{1}{4}$

1. Find a common denominator. Since 5×4 is 20, 20 is a common denominator for $\frac{2}{5}$ and $\frac{1}{4}$.

2. Change to equivalent fractions.

$$\frac{2}{5} = \frac{8}{20} \qquad \frac{1}{4} = \frac{5}{20}$$

3. Compare. Since $\frac{8}{20}$ is greater than $\frac{5}{20}$, $\frac{2}{5}$ is greater than $\frac{1}{4}$.

$$\mathbf{\frac{2}{5} > \frac{1}{4}}$$

Change the fractions in each pair to equivalent fractions that have common denominators. Then compare the fractions by writing >, <, or = in the circles.

A $\frac{1}{3} \bigcirc \frac{3}{5}$ $\frac{1}{4} \bigcirc \frac{3}{6}$ $\frac{2}{3} \bigcirc \frac{1}{2}$ $\frac{3}{7} \bigcirc \frac{1}{10}$

B $\frac{3}{5} \bigcirc \frac{5}{12}$ $\frac{2}{3} \bigcirc \frac{3}{5}$ $\frac{3}{8} \bigcirc \frac{4}{7}$ $\frac{9}{10} \bigcirc \frac{5}{6}$

C $\frac{3}{4} \bigcirc \frac{4}{5}$ $\frac{1}{5} \bigcirc \frac{2}{7}$ $\frac{4}{9} \bigcirc \frac{2}{5}$ $\frac{5}{8} \bigcirc \frac{3}{11}$

Solve.

D Evan has 15 marbles. If $\frac{1}{3}$ of the marbles are blue and $\frac{2}{5}$ are yellow, does he have more blue marbles or yellow marbles?

____

E Ashley has a quilt made up of 24 squares. If $\frac{3}{8}$ of the squares are red and $\frac{1}{4}$ of the squares are purple, does the quilt have more red squares or purple squares?

____

Fractions and Decimals • 5–6 © 2007 Creative Teaching Press

Name _____ Date _____

Mixed Numbers and Improper Fractions

A mixed number is made up of a whole number and a fraction. An improper fraction has a numerator that is greater than or equal to the denominator.

mixed number → $2\frac{1}{3} = \frac{7}{3}$ ← improper fraction

To change a mixed number to an improper fraction, first change the whole number to fraction form. Do this by multiplying the denominator and the whole number. Then add the fractional part of the mixed number to get the total number of parts.

$2\frac{1}{3}$ → Think 2 × 3 to get the number of thirds. ← $\frac{6}{3}$

Then add ⅔ and ⅓ to get ⅞.

Change the mixed numbers to improper fractions or whole numbers.

A $2\frac{1}{4} =$ _____ $4\frac{1}{4} =$ _____ $3\frac{2}{9} =$ _____ $2\frac{5}{8} =$ _____

B $1\frac{4}{5} =$ _____ $2\frac{3}{7} =$ _____ $5\frac{4}{11} =$ _____ $3\frac{7}{12} =$ _____

C $6\frac{3}{4} =$ _____ $5\frac{3}{10} =$ _____ $3\frac{4}{9} =$ _____ $10\frac{2}{5} =$ _____

To change an improper fraction to a mixed number, divide the numerator by the denominator to find the whole number. Write the remainder as a fraction.

$\frac{7}{3}$ → $3\overline{)7}$ → 2 ← number of wholes

-6

$2\frac{1}{3}$ ← $\frac{}{1}$ ← number of thirds left over

Change the mixed numbers to improper fractions or whole numbers.

D $\frac{9}{2} =$ $\frac{12}{3} =$ $\frac{13}{4} =$ $\frac{12}{7} =$

E $\frac{15}{5} =$ $\frac{19}{8} =$ $\frac{51}{10} =$ $\frac{32}{5} =$

F $\frac{29}{3} =$ $\frac{55}{8} =$ $\frac{24}{3} =$ $\frac{41}{12} =$

Fractions and Decimals • 5–6 © 2007 Creative Teaching Press

Adding and Subtracting Fractions with Like Denominators

When adding or subtracting fractions that have the same denominators, add or subtract the numerators and keep the denominators the same. Write the answers in simplest form.

$$\frac{1}{6} + \frac{2}{6} = \frac{3}{6} = \frac{1}{2}$$

$$\frac{9}{12} - \frac{5}{12} = \frac{4}{12} = \frac{1}{3}$$

$$\frac{4}{5} + \frac{4}{5} = \frac{8}{5} = 1\frac{3}{5}$$

Add or subtract the fractions. Write the answers in simplest form.

A $\dfrac{1}{5} + \dfrac{2}{5} =$ $\qquad$ $\dfrac{5}{9} + \dfrac{1}{9} =$ $\qquad$ $\dfrac{2}{7} + \dfrac{3}{7} =$

B $\dfrac{11}{12} - \dfrac{2}{12} =$ $\qquad$ $\dfrac{7}{8} - \dfrac{3}{8} =$ $\qquad$ $\dfrac{10}{11} - \dfrac{2}{11} =$

C $\dfrac{4}{7} + \dfrac{9}{7} =$ $\qquad$ $\dfrac{8}{9} - \dfrac{3}{9} =$ $\qquad$ $\dfrac{13}{15} - \dfrac{7}{15} =$

D $\dfrac{7}{10} - \dfrac{3}{10} =$ $\qquad$ $\dfrac{6}{8} + \dfrac{4}{8} =$ $\qquad$ $\dfrac{3}{6} + \dfrac{5}{6} =$

E $\dfrac{9}{14} - \dfrac{2}{14} =$ $\qquad$ $\dfrac{10}{12} - \dfrac{2}{12} =$ $\qquad$ $\dfrac{8}{9} + \dfrac{8}{9} =$

Solve. Write the answers in simplest form.

F Maria lives $\frac{11}{12}$ mile from the airport. Andy lives $\frac{9}{12}$ mile from the airport. How much farther is Maria's home from the airport than Andy's home?

G Ryan has 3 toy planes. Each one is ¾ foot long. If he lines up the planes so that they touch one another, how long will the line be?

_____

_____

Fractions and Decimals • 5–6 © 2007 Creative Teaching Press

Name _____ Date _____

Least Common Denominator

Before you can add or subtract fractions that have different denominators, you have to find a common denominator. The least common denominator (LCD) is the smallest denominator you can use. To find the LCD, you need to find a common multiple of the denominators.

Example: Add ⅙ and ⅛. $\dfrac{1}{6} + \dfrac{1}{8} =$

1. List the multiples of 6 and 8.

Multiples of 6:
6 12 18 ㉔ 30 36

Multiples of 8:
8 16 ㉔ 32 40 48

2. The least common multiple is 24. Use that as the common denominator.

3. Find equivalent fractions for ⅙ and ⅛, using 24 as the denominator.

$$\frac{1}{6} = \frac{4}{24} \qquad \frac{1}{8} = \frac{3}{24}$$

4. Rewrite the problem using the equivalent fractions, and solve.

$$\frac{1}{6} + \frac{1}{8} = \frac{4}{24} + \frac{3}{24} = \frac{7}{24}$$

Rewrite each problem using the least common denominator. Then solve. Write the answers in simplest form.

A $\dfrac{1}{4} + \dfrac{1}{6} =$

B $\dfrac{1}{3} + \dfrac{1}{6} =$

C $\dfrac{11}{12} - \dfrac{1}{4} =$

D $\dfrac{1}{2} + \dfrac{5}{12} =$

E $\dfrac{7}{8} - \dfrac{5}{6} =$

F $\dfrac{13}{15} - \dfrac{2}{3} =$

G $\dfrac{17}{20} - \dfrac{3}{4} =$

H $\dfrac{4}{10} + \dfrac{1}{2} =$

I $\dfrac{3}{4} - \dfrac{3}{10} =$

J $\dfrac{3}{10} + \dfrac{3}{8} =$

K $\dfrac{2}{9} + \dfrac{7}{12} =$

L $\dfrac{5}{9} + \dfrac{2}{6} =$

Adding and Subtracting Fractions with Unlike Denominators

When adding or subtracting fractions that have different denominators, first change the fractions to equivalent fractions that have the same denominators.

1. You can quickly find a common denominator by multiplying the two denominators.

$$\frac{1}{3} + \frac{2}{5} \rightarrow 3 \times 5 = 15$$

You can use 15 as your common denominator.

2. Rename the fractions, using the common denominator.

$$\frac{1}{3} = \frac{5}{15} \qquad \frac{2}{5} = \frac{6}{15}$$

3. Rewrite the problem and solve.

$$\frac{5}{15} + \frac{6}{15} = \frac{11}{15}$$

Rewrite the problems using common denominators. Solve. Write the answers in simplest form.

A $\frac{1}{2} + \frac{1}{3} =$

B $\frac{1}{4} + \frac{3}{5} =$

C $\frac{2}{5} + \frac{1}{6} =$

D $\frac{2}{3} - \frac{1}{2} =$

E $\frac{7}{8} - \frac{1}{3} =$

F $\frac{3}{4} - \frac{3}{8} =$

G $\frac{2}{3} + \frac{1}{12} =$

H $\frac{1}{2} - \frac{2}{5} =$

I $\frac{7}{9} - \frac{1}{3} =$

J $\frac{5}{8} + \frac{1}{6} =$

K $\frac{11}{16} - \frac{1}{2} =$

L $\frac{1}{2} + \frac{3}{10} =$

Fractions and Decimals · 5–6 © 2007 Creative Teaching Press

Adding Mixed Numbers

When adding mixed numbers, first make sure the fractional parts have common denominators. Next, add the fractions. Then, add the whole numbers.

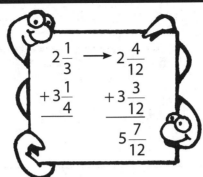

$$2\frac{1}{3} \rightarrow 2\frac{4}{12}$$
$$+3\frac{1}{4} \quad +3\frac{3}{12}$$
$$\overline{\qquad} \quad \overline{5\frac{7}{12}}$$

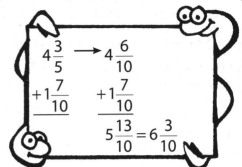

$$4\frac{3}{5} \rightarrow 4\frac{6}{10}$$
$$+1\frac{7}{10} \quad +1\frac{7}{10}$$
$$\overline{\qquad} \quad \overline{5\frac{13}{10}=6\frac{3}{10}}$$

Add. Write the answers in simplest form. The first one is done for you.

A $2\frac{1}{2} \rightarrow 2\frac{4}{8}$ $\qquad\qquad$ $3\frac{1}{3}$ $\qquad\qquad$ $4\frac{9}{12}$

$\quad +5\frac{1}{8} \quad +5\frac{1}{8}$ $\qquad\quad$ $+3\frac{2}{15}$ $\qquad\qquad$ $+2\frac{4}{6}$

$\qquad\qquad\quad 7\frac{5}{8}$

B $4\frac{2}{7}$ $\qquad\qquad\qquad$ $2\frac{3}{5}$ $\qquad\qquad\qquad$ $6\frac{4}{6}$

$\quad +6\frac{5}{14}$ $\qquad\qquad$ $+1\frac{1}{6}$ $\qquad\qquad$ $+5\frac{1}{3}$

C $4\frac{1}{2}$ $\qquad\qquad\qquad$ $2\frac{8}{12}$ $\qquad\qquad\qquad$ $5\frac{1}{6}$

$\quad +2\frac{2}{5}$ $\qquad\qquad$ $+6\frac{3}{8}$ $\qquad\qquad$ $+2\frac{2}{3}$

Solve.

D A pet store owner had two snakes. One was 1¾ feet long, and the other was 1⅝ feet long. If the snakes were placed end-to-end to form a line, how long would the line be?

_____

E A snake crawled 5 ⅔ yards across the field. Then it crawled 3 2/15 yards more. How far did it crawl in all?

_____

Fractions and Decimals • 5–6 © 2007 Creative Teaching Press

Name _____ Date _____

Subtracting Mixed Numbers

When subtracting mixed numbers, subtract the fraction first. (You may need to regroup before you subtract.) Then, subtract the whole numbers.

$$6\frac{3}{4} \longrightarrow 6\frac{3}{4}$$
$$-1\frac{1}{2} \qquad -1\frac{2}{4}$$
$$\overline{\qquad\qquad 5\frac{1}{4}}$$

$$7\frac{1}{5} \longrightarrow 6\frac{6}{5}$$
$$-2\frac{3}{5} \qquad -2\frac{3}{5}$$
$$\overline{\qquad\qquad 4\frac{3}{5}}$$

$$6 \longrightarrow 5\frac{4}{4}$$
$$-3\frac{1}{4} \qquad -3\frac{1}{4}$$
$$\overline{\qquad\qquad 2\frac{3}{4}}$$

Subtract. Regroup first if needed. Write the answers in simplest form.

A
$$2\frac{1}{2}$$
$$-1\frac{1}{4}$$

$$3\frac{5}{6}$$
$$-2\frac{1}{3}$$

$$5\frac{3}{9}$$
$$-1\frac{2}{3}$$

B
$$4\frac{5}{7}$$
$$-3\frac{1}{4}$$

$$6\frac{3}{10}$$
$$-2\frac{4}{5}$$

$$7\frac{3}{8}$$
$$-6\frac{3}{4}$$

C
$$9\frac{2}{3}$$
$$-5\frac{4}{6}$$

$$8\frac{5}{12}$$
$$-3\frac{1}{4}$$

$$4\frac{5}{6}$$
$$-2\frac{3}{5}$$

Solve.

D Kent is 2 ½ inches shorter than Brian. Brian is 59 ¼ inches tall. How tall is Kent?

_____

E Kelly skated 1⅔ hours. Linda skated 2 ⅙ hours. How much longer did Linda skate than Kelly?

_____

Fractions and Decimals • 5–6 • © 2007 Creative Teaching Press

Multiplying Fractions

To multiply fractions, multiply the numerators together and multiply the denominators together.

$$\frac{2}{5} \times \frac{3}{6} = \frac{6}{30} = \frac{1}{5}$$

Multiply. Write the answers in simplest form.

A $\frac{1}{3} \times \frac{1}{4} =$ $\frac{2}{7} \times \frac{1}{4} =$ $\frac{3}{5} \times \frac{1}{4} =$

B $\frac{3}{4} \times \frac{3}{4} =$ $\frac{5}{8} \times \frac{1}{2} =$ $\frac{6}{11} \times \frac{2}{3} =$

C $\frac{3}{4} \times \frac{5}{6} =$ $\frac{1}{4} \times \frac{5}{7} =$ $\frac{5}{9} \times \frac{3}{10} =$

D $\frac{1}{2} \times \frac{5}{11} =$ $\frac{2}{3} \times \frac{3}{10} =$ $\frac{3}{4} \times \frac{5}{12} =$

E $\frac{2}{3} \times \frac{3}{4} =$ $\frac{1}{2} \times \frac{8}{9} =$ $\frac{7}{8} \times \frac{2}{7} =$

Solve.

F A pizza was divided into fourths. Jack ate ½ of one of the fourths. What part of the pizza did he eat?

_____

G A cake was divided into thirds. Lisa ate ⅓ of one of the thirds. What part of the cake did she eat?

_____

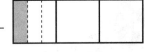

Multiplying Fractions—Canceling

If there is the same number in the numerator of one fraction and the denominator of the other fraction, you can cancel them out. Canceling makes multiplying easier.

Here's why canceling works: $\dfrac{3}{5} \times \dfrac{2}{3}$ can be changed to $\dfrac{3 \times 2}{5 \times 3}$

Then $\dfrac{3 \times 2}{5 \times 3}$ can be changed this way: $\dfrac{3 \times 2}{5 \times 3} = \dfrac{3}{3} \times \dfrac{2}{5} = 1 \times \dfrac{2}{5} = \dfrac{2}{5}$

Use canceling to multiply. Write the answers in simplest form.

A $\dfrac{1}{4} \times \dfrac{4}{5} =$ $\dfrac{2}{8} \times \dfrac{1}{2} =$ $\dfrac{3}{7} \times \dfrac{7}{10} =$

B $\dfrac{5}{6} \times \dfrac{1}{5} =$ $\dfrac{9}{10} \times \dfrac{7}{9} =$ $\dfrac{2}{5} \times \dfrac{1}{2} =$

C $\dfrac{6}{11} \times \dfrac{5}{6} =$ $\dfrac{3}{7} \times \dfrac{2}{3} =$ $\dfrac{8}{15} \times \dfrac{7}{8} =$

If the numerator of one fraction and the denominator of the other fraction have common factors, you can use canceling, too. To do this, divide that numerator and denominator by their greatest common factor.

Here's why it works:

$$\dfrac{3}{4} \times \dfrac{8}{11} = \dfrac{3 \times 8}{4 \times 11} = \dfrac{8 \times 3}{4 \times 11} = \dfrac{8}{4} \times \dfrac{3}{11} = \dfrac{2}{1} \times \dfrac{3}{11} = \dfrac{6}{11}$$

$$\dfrac{3}{4} \times \dfrac{8}{11} \rightarrow \dfrac{3}{\underset{1}{4}} \times \dfrac{\overset{2}{8}}{11} = \dfrac{6}{11}$$

Use canceling to multiply. Write the answers in simplest form.

D $\dfrac{1}{2} \times \dfrac{4}{5} =$ $\dfrac{2}{3} \times \dfrac{6}{7} =$ $\dfrac{1}{9} \times \dfrac{3}{4} =$

E $\dfrac{5}{8} \times \dfrac{7}{15} =$ $\dfrac{3}{8} \times \dfrac{5}{12} =$ $\dfrac{4}{5} \times \dfrac{7}{12} =$

F $\dfrac{2}{3} \times \dfrac{3}{4} =$ $\dfrac{3}{10} \times \dfrac{5}{9} =$ $\dfrac{8}{10} \times \dfrac{10}{12} =$

Fractions and Decimals • 5–6 © 2007 Creative Teaching Press

Multiplying Fractions with Whole Numbers and Mixed Numbers

When multiplying fractions with whole numbers or mixed numbers, change each whole number or mixed number to an improper fraction first. Then multiply.

$$\frac{3}{4} \times 3 = \frac{3}{4} \times \frac{3}{1} = \frac{9}{4} = 2\frac{1}{4}$$

$$\frac{4}{5} \times 2\frac{2}{3} = \frac{4}{5} \times \frac{8}{3} = \frac{32}{15} = 2\frac{2}{15}$$

Multiply. Write the answers in simplest form.

A $\frac{1}{2} \times 2\frac{1}{2} =$

B $\frac{2}{3} \times 9 =$

C $\frac{5}{7} \times 4\frac{1}{2} =$

D $3\frac{1}{4} \times 2 =$

E $5\frac{2}{9} \times \frac{3}{5} =$

F $\frac{3}{8} \times 1\frac{1}{6} =$

G $\frac{1}{3} \times 6\frac{1}{2} =$

H $\frac{9}{10} \times 2\frac{2}{3} =$

I $3 \times \frac{5}{6} =$

J $\frac{1}{4} \times 3\frac{1}{5} =$

K $\frac{2}{7} \times 14 =$

L $\frac{3}{10} \times 1\frac{2}{3} =$

M $\frac{3}{4} \times 5 =$

N $2\frac{1}{4} \times \frac{8}{9} =$

Fractional Parts of a Number

There are 6 buttons. One-third of the buttons are blue. Two-thirds of them are yellow. How many buttons are blue and how many are yellow? To find the answer, you can put the buttons in three equal groups. Then, count the number of buttons in one group to find ⅓ of 6. Count the buttons in two of the groups to find ⅔ of 6.

You can also multiply to find the answers.

$\frac{1}{3}$ of 6 → $\frac{1}{3} \times \frac{6}{1} = \frac{6}{3} = \textbf{2}$ $\frac{2}{3}$ of 6 → $\frac{2}{3} \times \frac{6}{1} = \frac{12}{3} = \textbf{4}$ $\frac{1}{3}$ of 6 = **2** $\frac{2}{3}$ of 6 = **4**

Solve. Use the pictures to help you.

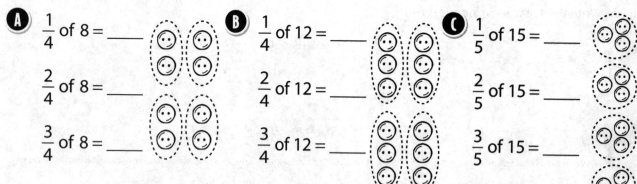

A $\frac{1}{4}$ of 8 = _____

$\frac{2}{4}$ of 8 = _____

$\frac{3}{4}$ of 8 = _____

B $\frac{1}{4}$ of 12 = _____

$\frac{2}{4}$ of 12 = _____

$\frac{3}{4}$ of 12 = _____

C $\frac{1}{5}$ of 15 = _____

$\frac{2}{5}$ of 15 = _____

$\frac{3}{5}$ of 15 = _____

$\frac{4}{5}$ of 15 = _____

Rewrite each problem as a multiplication problem. Then solve.

D $\frac{1}{2}$ of 8 = $\frac{1}{3}$ of 9 = $\frac{1}{6}$ of 12 =

E $\frac{2}{3}$ of 12 = $\frac{3}{4}$ of 16 = $\frac{5}{6}$ of 12 =

F $\frac{3}{7}$ of 14 = $\frac{8}{9}$ of 18 = $\frac{5}{6}$ of 18 =

Solve.

G There are 24 buttons in a box. Two-thirds are white. How many buttons are white?

_____

H There are 15 buttons on the table. Three-fifths are square-shaped. How many buttons are shaped like a square?

_____

Fractions and Decimals • 5–6 © 2007 Creative Teaching Press

Reciprocals

The reciprocal of a fraction is the fraction flipped upside down. For example, the reciprocal of ⅔ is 3/2, and the reciprocal of ¼ is 4/1, or 4. The product of a fraction and its reciprocal is 1.

$$\frac{2}{3} \times \frac{3}{2} = \frac{\cancel{2}^{1}}{\cancel{3}_{1}} \times \frac{\cancel{3}^{1}}{\cancel{2}_{1}} = 1 \qquad \frac{1}{4} \times \frac{4}{1} = \frac{\cancel{1}^{1}}{\cancel{4}_{1}} \times \frac{\cancel{4}^{1}}{\cancel{1}_{1}} = 1$$

Write the reciprocal of each fraction.

A $\frac{3}{7}$ _____ $\frac{4}{5}$ _____ $\frac{1}{3}$ _____ $\frac{2}{9}$ _____

B $\frac{1}{8}$ _____ $\frac{7}{10}$ _____ $\frac{11}{15}$ _____ $\frac{1}{6}$ _____

C $\frac{5}{9}$ _____ $\frac{11}{12}$ _____ $\frac{1}{10}$ _____ $\frac{4}{13}$ _____

To find the reciprocal of a mixed number, first change the mixed number to an improper fraction. Then, flip the fraction. For example, to find the reciprocal of 1 ⅖, change the number to 7/5. Then, flip it to get 5/7 as the reciprocal.

Write the reciprocal of each mixed number.

D $1\frac{3}{4}$ _____ $1\frac{1}{6}$ _____ $2\frac{3}{8}$ _____

E $3\frac{1}{10}$ _____ $4\frac{2}{5}$ _____ $3\frac{1}{4}$ _____

F $10\frac{1}{2}$ _____ $6\frac{2}{3}$ _____ $5\frac{5}{8}$ _____

Dividing Fractions

Did you know that dividing by a number is the same as multiplying by its reciprocal? Just watch!

$$10 \div \mathbf{2} = \mathbf{5}$$

$$10 \times \frac{\mathbf{1}}{\mathbf{2}} = \frac{10}{2} = \mathbf{5}$$

Dividing by 2 is the same as multiplying by ½.

To divide fractions, simply change the division sign to multiplication and flip the divisor.

Example: $\dfrac{5}{8} \div \dfrac{1}{2} = \dfrac{5}{8} \times \dfrac{2}{1} = \dfrac{10}{8} = 1\dfrac{2}{8} = 1\dfrac{1}{4}$

Then, check your answer: $1\dfrac{1}{4} \times \dfrac{1}{2} = \dfrac{5}{4} \times \dfrac{1}{2} = \dfrac{5}{8}$

Divide. Check your answers using multiplication.

A $\dfrac{1}{2} \div \dfrac{1}{4} =$

Check :

B $\dfrac{1}{3} \div 3 =$

Check :

C $\dfrac{4}{5} \div \dfrac{1}{2} =$

Check :

D $\dfrac{1}{2} \div \dfrac{4}{9} =$

Check :

E $\dfrac{1}{7} \div \dfrac{1}{18} =$

Check :

F $\dfrac{5}{9} \div \dfrac{3}{4} =$

Check :

G $\dfrac{7}{8} \div \dfrac{1}{8} =$

Check :

H $\dfrac{1}{2} \div \dfrac{3}{10} =$

Check :

I $\dfrac{5}{6} \div \dfrac{5}{8} =$

Check :

J $\dfrac{9}{10} \div \dfrac{2}{5} =$

Check :

Solve.

K Tiffany bought ¾ yard of fabric to make some doll clothes. She needs ⅛ yard to make one outfit. How many outfits can she make?

_____

L Rob had a board that was ⅚ yard long. He divided the board into three equal pieces. How long was each board?

_____

Fractions and Decimals • 5–6 © 2007 Creative Teaching Press

Dividing with Mixed Numbers

When dividing with mixed numbers or whole numbers, first change the mixed number or whole number to an improper fraction. Then divide the same way you would divide fractions.

$$1\frac{1}{2} \div \frac{3}{4} = \frac{3}{2} \div \frac{3}{4} = \frac{3}{2} \times \frac{4}{3} = \frac{12}{6} = 2$$

$$1\frac{1}{2} \div 1\frac{1}{5} = \frac{3}{2} \div \frac{6}{5} = \frac{3}{2} \times \frac{5}{6} = \frac{15}{12} = 1\frac{3}{12} = 1\frac{1}{4}$$

Divide. Write the answers in simplest form.

A $1\frac{2}{3} \div \frac{1}{6} =$

F $4\frac{2}{3} \div 1\frac{1}{4} =$

B $\frac{3}{5} \div 1\frac{1}{3} =$

G $3\frac{3}{10} \div 3 =$

C $2\frac{1}{3} \div 1\frac{1}{2} =$

H $2\frac{5}{6} \div 1\frac{1}{2} =$

D $4\frac{1}{5} \div 7 =$

I $5\frac{4}{9} \div 7 =$

E $1\frac{9}{10} \div 2 =$

J $6 \div 3\frac{1}{2} =$

Solve.

K Alina had some yarn that was 10 feet long. She cut it into pieces that were ⅔ foot long. How many pieces did she get?

L Sam had 2 ¾ pounds of nails. He put an equal number of nails into four containers. How many pounds of nails did he put in each container?

_____

_____

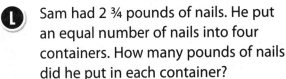

Name ______________________________ Date ______________

Review of Fraction Concepts

Write equivalent fractions.

A $\frac{2}{3} = \frac{_}{6}$ $\frac{2}{5} = \frac{_}{15}$ $\frac{20}{25} = \frac{_}{5}$ $\frac{6}{18} = \frac{_}{6}$

Write each fraction in simplest form.

B $\frac{12}{15}$ ______ $\frac{9}{12}$ ______ $\frac{20}{32}$ ______ $\frac{9}{21}$ ______

Look at the fractions in each set. Write them in order from the least to the greatest.

C $\frac{1}{3}, \frac{1}{8}, \frac{1}{5}$ ______ **D** $\frac{3}{4}, \frac{1}{4}, \frac{3}{8}$ ______ **E** $\frac{5}{6}, \frac{2}{6}, \frac{2}{3}$ ______

F $\frac{1}{5}, \frac{3}{5}, \frac{4}{10}$ ______ **G** $\frac{2}{3}, \frac{5}{9}, \frac{2}{9}$ ______ **H** $\frac{3}{4}, \frac{5}{12}, \frac{1}{2}$ ______

Change the mixed numbers to improper fractions.

I $1\frac{2}{5}$ ______ $5\frac{2}{3}$ ______ $4\frac{3}{4}$ ______ $8\frac{1}{2}$ ______

Change the improper fractions to mixed numbers.

J $\frac{19}{2}$ ______ $\frac{16}{4}$ ______ $\frac{15}{8}$ ______ $\frac{27}{5}$ ______

Solve.

K What is $\frac{1}{4}$ of 12? ______

L What is $\frac{2}{3}$ of 15? ______

M What is $\frac{3}{5}$ of 20? ______

N What is $\frac{4}{7}$ of 21? ______

Solve.

O Lauren has 24 felt squares. If $\frac{1}{3}$ of the squares were blue and $\frac{3}{8}$ were red, would Lauren have more blue squares or red squares?

______

P Matthew jogged $\frac{5}{6}$ mile on Monday. He jogged $\frac{7}{9}$ mile on Tuesday. On which day did he jog farther?

______

Fractions and Decimals • 5–6 © 2007 Creative Teaching Press

Fractions—Addition and Subtraction Review

Add or subtract. Write the answers in simplest form.

A $\dfrac{4}{9} + \dfrac{2}{9} =$ $\dfrac{11}{12} - \dfrac{5}{12} =$ $\dfrac{13}{16} - \dfrac{1}{16} =$

B $\dfrac{1}{2} + \dfrac{1}{4} =$ $\dfrac{7}{8} - \dfrac{3}{4} =$ $\dfrac{7}{10} + \dfrac{3}{5} =$

C $\dfrac{2}{3} + \dfrac{1}{4} =$ $\dfrac{5}{9} - \dfrac{1}{6} =$ $\dfrac{7}{8} - \dfrac{5}{12} =$

Add or subtract. Write the answers in simplest form.

D $\begin{array}{r} 4\frac{1}{3} \\ +\,2\frac{2}{3} \\ \hline \end{array}$ $\begin{array}{r} 2\frac{5}{6} \\ +\,1\frac{1}{3} \\ \hline \end{array}$ $\begin{array}{r} 6\frac{5}{9} \\ -\,3\frac{2}{9} \\ \hline \end{array}$

E $\begin{array}{r} 7\frac{4}{8} \\ -\,6\frac{1}{4} \\ \hline \end{array}$ $\begin{array}{r} 9 \\ -\,3\frac{7}{10} \\ \hline \end{array}$ $\begin{array}{r} 5\frac{1}{2} \\ +\,3\frac{2}{3} \\ \hline \end{array}$

F $\begin{array}{r} 3\frac{2}{5} \\ -\,1\frac{3}{4} \\ \hline \end{array}$ $\begin{array}{r} 6\frac{7}{8} \\ +\,5\frac{5}{6} \\ \hline \end{array}$ $\begin{array}{r} 8\frac{1}{6} \\ -\,2\frac{4}{9} \\ \hline \end{array}$

Solve.

G A baker needs 2 ¼ cups of flour to make a batch of cookies and 2 ⅜ cups of flour to make a cake. How much flour will she need to make three batches of cookies and two cakes?

_____

H Scott spends 1⅓ hours on homework each day. Kim spends 1¾ hours on homework each day. After two days, how many more hours of homework will Kim have done than Scott?

_____

Fractions and Decimals • 5–6 • © 2007 Creative Teaching Press

Fractions—Multiplication and Division Review

Multiply. Write the answers in simplest form.

A $\dfrac{2}{3} \times \dfrac{1}{4} =$

B $\dfrac{7}{8} \times \dfrac{3}{4} =$

C $1\dfrac{1}{2} \times 3 =$

D $2\dfrac{1}{6} \times 2\dfrac{1}{2} =$

E $\dfrac{4}{9} \times 18 =$

F $1\dfrac{1}{2} \times 3\dfrac{1}{3} =$

G $5 \times \dfrac{7}{10} =$

H $4\dfrac{3}{5} \times \dfrac{5}{7} =$

Divide. Write the answers in simplest form.

I $\dfrac{9}{2} \div \dfrac{1}{2} =$

J $3\dfrac{1}{6} \div 1\dfrac{1}{3} =$

K $\dfrac{9}{10} \div \dfrac{3}{5} =$

L $6 \div \dfrac{4}{5} =$

M $\dfrac{12}{15} \div 3 =$

N $2\dfrac{1}{8} \div 1\dfrac{1}{2} =$

O $4\dfrac{2}{7} \div 5 =$

P $8 \div 2\dfrac{2}{5} =$

Fractions and Decimals • 5–6 © 2007 Creative Teaching Press

Decimals and Place Value

Decimals express multiples of tenths (⅒; ⅟₁₀₀; ⅟₁,₀₀₀; and so on).

$$\frac{3}{10} = 0.3 \qquad \frac{34}{100} = 0.34 \qquad \frac{347}{1,000} = 0.347$$

A place value chart can help you understand decimals. The value of a number to the right of the decimal point is less than 1.

Decimal Point

Whole Numbers			
thousands	hundreds	tens	ones
			0

Decimals		
tenths	hundredths	thousandths
3	4	7

Write a fraction and a decimal for each amount.

A 9 tenths _____

B 3 hundredths _____

C 4 tenths _____

D 9 thousandths _____

E 21 hundredths _____

F 84 hundredths _____

G 73 hundredths _____

H 35 thousandths _____

I 562 thousandths _____

J 8 tenths _____

K 918 thousandths _____

L 405 thousandths _____

Write the value of the underlined digit in each number.

M 3.2<u>5</u> _____

N 25.<u>5</u>07 _____

O <u>7</u>2.56 _____

P 712.45<u>9</u> _____

Q 6.0<u>7</u> _____

R <u>3</u>04.865 _____

S 5.38<u>2</u> _____

T <u>3</u>,569.043 _____

Fractions and Decimals • 5–6 © 2007 Creative Teaching Press

Matching Fractions and Decimals

Write the matching fractions.

A 0.5 _____   0.7 _____   0.23 _____   0.68 _____

B 0.317 _____   0.452 _____   0.08 _____   0.019 _____

C 0.4 _____   0.07 _____   0.003 _____   0.205 _____

Write the matching decimals.

D $\dfrac{2}{10}$ _____ $\dfrac{69}{100}$ _____ $\dfrac{237}{1,000}$ _____ $\dfrac{44}{100}$ _____

E $\dfrac{108}{1,000}$ _____ $\dfrac{47}{1,000}$ _____ $\dfrac{7}{100}$ _____ $\dfrac{9}{1,000}$ _____

F $\dfrac{2}{100}$ _____ $\dfrac{15}{100}$ _____ $\dfrac{6}{10}$ _____ $\dfrac{83}{1,000}$ _____

Write the matching mixed numbers.

G 5.3 _____   1.14 _____   2.507 _____   9.9 _____

H 7.09 _____   13.206 _____   4.003 _____   8.016 _____

Write the matching decimals.

I $6\dfrac{53}{100}$ _____ $8\dfrac{2}{10}$ _____ $9\dfrac{35}{1,000}$ _____ $10\dfrac{6}{100}$ _____

J $14\dfrac{8}{1,000}$ _____ $3\dfrac{2}{10}$ _____ $4\dfrac{71}{100}$ _____ $5\dfrac{1}{100}$ _____

Fractions and Decimals · 5–6 © 2007 Creative Teaching Press

Name _____ Date _____

Comparing Decimals

Placing one or more zeros to the right of a decimal does not affect its value.

$$0.3 = 0.30 = 0.300$$

$$\frac{3}{10} = \frac{30}{100} = \frac{300}{1,000}$$

When comparing decimals, add zeros whenever you need to so that all the decimals have the same number of digits to the right of the decimal point. This makes it easier to compare decimals.

Example: Which is greater—0.4 or 0.43?
1. Add 0 to the right of 0.4 to get 0.40.
2. Compare 0.40 and 0.43. Since ⁴³⁄₁₀₀ is greater than ⁴⁰⁄₁₀₀, 0.43 is greater.

Compare the decimals. Write >, <, or = in the circles.

A 0.6 ◯ 0.8   0.23 ◯ 0.21   0.5 ◯ 0.50   0.18 ◯ 0.81

B 0.09 ◯ 0.90   0.05 ◯ 0.008   0.034 ◯ 0.34   0.6 ◯ 0.600

C 1.03 ◯ 1.003   2.7 ◯ 2.700   1.3 ◯ 1.05   5.16 ◯ 5.163

Write the decimals in order from the least to the greatest.

D 0.357 _____
0.037 _____
0.75 _____
0.007 _____

E 0.05 _____
0.55 _____
0.555 _____
0.055 _____

F 1.23 _____
1.032 _____
1.302 _____
1.003 _____

G 0.42 _____
0.024 _____
0.4 _____
0.042 _____

H 5.79 _____
5.097 _____
5.07 _____
5.9 _____

I 8.11 _____
8.01 _____
8.011 _____
8.101 _____

Name _____ Date _____

Rounding Decimals

Rounding decimals is similar to rounding whole numbers. First, look at the place you want to round. Then, look at the digit to the right. Round up if the digit is 5 or more. If the digit is 4 or less keep the number the same.

Rounding 3.164 to the nearest hundredth means you need to decide if the number is closer to 3.16 or 3.17. Since the number to the right of the 6 is less than 5, round to 3.16.

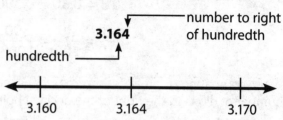

Round to the nearest tenth.

A 0.32 _____ 1.57 _____ 0.08 _____ 3.49 _____

B 2.78 _____ 0.92 _____ 4.31 _____ 6.75 _____

C 5.819 _____ 3.076 _____ 5.428 _____ 9.361 _____

Round to the nearest hundredth.

D 0.324 _____ 0.865 _____ 2.956 _____ 3.208 _____

E 1.765 _____ 5.321 _____ 4.005 _____ 9.246 _____

F 8.203 _____ 6.984 _____ 11.627 _____ 15.376 _____

Round to the nearest whole number.

G 4.5 _____ 7.3 _____ 3.1 _____ 8.7 _____

H 6.32 _____ 5.04 _____ 8.52 _____ 7.99 _____

I 14.512 _____ 2.399 _____ 6.084 _____ 20.072 _____

Solve.

J A river is 0.483 mile wide. What is its width to the nearest tenth of a mile?

_____

K A runner ran around 1.562 miles. What was the distance rounded to the nearest hundredth of a mile?

_____

Fractions and Decimals • 5–6 © 2007 Creative Teaching Press

Adding Decimals

Add decimals by adding the columns one at a time, starting with the one at the far right. Add zeros if the number of digits after the decimal point is not the same. Regroup if needed.

$$2.743 \longrightarrow 2.743 \longrightarrow \overset{1}{}2.743$$
$$+\ 3.51 \qquad +\ 3.51\mathbf{0} \qquad +\ 3.510$$
$$\overline{} \qquad \overline{} \qquad \overline{6.253}$$

Add.

A

0.06	3.29	7.156	2.58	8.13
+ 4.9	+ 0.8	+ 2.903	+ 9.6	+ 0.977

B

7	9.899	4.16	10.003	5.2
+ 0.35	+ 0.34	+ 0.008	+ 1.999	+ 1.683

C

23.1	14.089	9.37	15.36	4.607
+ 5.86	+ 3.54	+ 12	+ 7.085	+ 8.73

D

15.14	8.03	9.3	4.5	8.01
6.8	12.54	50.03	4.56	1.8
+ 20.932	+ 16.8	+ 18.9	+ 4.567	+ 6.325

Solve.

 E Brandon went on a biking trip with his friends. He traveled 25.68 miles one way. What was the total number of miles he biked if he came back the same way?

 F The Taylors went on a car trip. Mr. Taylor drove the first 86.55 miles. Then, Mrs. Taylor drove the last 72.75 miles. How many miles did they drive altogether?

_____   _____

Subtracting Decimals

Subtract decimals by subtracting one column at a time, starting with the far right. If you need to, add zeros as placeholders so that the number of digits after the decimal point is the same. Regroup if needed.

$$\begin{array}{r} 8.76 \\ -\,3.327 \\ \hline \end{array} \rightarrow \begin{array}{r} 8.76\mathbf{0} \\ -\,3.327 \\ \hline \end{array} \rightarrow \begin{array}{r} {}^{5\ 10}\\ 8.7\cancel{6}\cancel{0} \\ -\,3.327 \\ \hline 5.433 \end{array}$$

Subtract.

A
4.98	2.65	12.5	8.007	10.34
− 1.3	− 0.09	− 8.36	− 5.1	− 6.7

B
3.07	15.82	43.15	25.3	0.069
− 1.684	− 7.66	− 9.684	− 8.77	− 0.03

C
45	68	27.056	36.08	0.8
− 21.4	− 19.241	− 3.84	− 19.2	− 0.051

D
37.06	12.8	25.07	50	18.635
− 3.492	− 9.37	− 6.883	− 9.99	− 2.7

Solve.

 E Kevin's flight lasted 5.9 hours. Brett's flight lasted 8.25 hours. How much longer was Brett's flight than Kevin's?

_____

 F Mandy lives 62.3 miles away from her grandmother and 25.78 miles from her uncle. How many miles farther is her grandmother's home than her uncle's?

_____

Fractions and Decimals • 5–6 © 2007 Creative Teaching Press

Name _____ Date _____

Multiplying Whole Numbers and Decimals

When multiplying a whole number and a decimal, first multiply without worrying about the decimal points. Once you have your product, put in the decimal point. Place the point so that the number of decimal places in the product equals the total number of decimal places in the factor.

^{1}0.4
× 3

1.2

See what happens when you change the decimals to fractions.

^{1}1.25
× 3

3.75

See what happens when you change the decimals to fractions.

$$\frac{4}{10} \times 3 = \frac{12}{10} = 1\frac{2}{10} = \mathbf{1.2}$$

$$1\frac{25}{100} \times 3 = \frac{125}{100} \times 3 = \frac{375}{100} = 3\frac{75}{100} = \mathbf{3.75}$$

Multiply.

A

0.6	0.9	0.3	0.42	0.26
× 7	× 8	× 5	× 3	× 2

B

1.51	2.34	6.12	0.98	3.26
× 5	× 7	× 4	× 7	× 9

C

4.124	6.359	7.111	8.623	9.132
× 2	× 4	× 8	× 3	× 6

D

0.876	1.23	3.8	3.594	8.72
× 4	× 7	× 9	× 9	× 8

Solve.

E Melissa has 6 packages. Each package weighs 8.3 ounces. What is the total weight of the packages?

F Richard runs 2.25 miles every day. How far does he run in a week?

_____

_____

Name _____ Date _____

Multiplying Decimals by Decimals

When multiplying decimals, don't worry about the decimal points at first. Just multiply the factors. Then, once you have your product, put in the decimal point. The number of decimal places in the product must equal the total number of decimal places in the factors.

$$\begin{array}{r} 1.2 \\ \times\, 0.3 \\ \hline \end{array}$$

$$\begin{array}{r} 1.2 \\ \times\, 0.3 \\ \hline 36 \end{array}$$

Think: $3 \times 12 = 36$

$$\begin{array}{r} 1.2 \\ \times\, 0.3 \\ \hline 0.36 \end{array}$$ ← total of 2 decimal places

2 decimal places

Multiply.

A

$$\begin{array}{r} 0.9 \\ \times\, 0.9 \\ \hline \end{array}$$
$$\begin{array}{r} 4.2 \\ \times\, 0.1 \\ \hline \end{array}$$
$$\begin{array}{r} 0.8 \\ \times\, 0.4 \\ \hline \end{array}$$
$$\begin{array}{r} 2.2 \\ \times\, 0.3 \\ \hline \end{array}$$
$$\begin{array}{r} 1.6 \\ \times\, 0.3 \\ \hline \end{array}$$

B

$$\begin{array}{r} 0.35 \\ \times\, 0.5 \\ \hline \end{array}$$
$$\begin{array}{r} 0.64 \\ \times\, 0.7 \\ \hline \end{array}$$
$$\begin{array}{r} 0.02 \\ \times\, 0.8 \\ \hline \end{array}$$
$$\begin{array}{r} 0.76 \\ \times\, 0.3 \\ \hline \end{array}$$
$$\begin{array}{r} 1.52 \\ \times\, 0.9 \\ \hline \end{array}$$

C

$$\begin{array}{r} 1.2 \\ \times\, 1.2 \\ \hline \end{array}$$
$$\begin{array}{r} 2.63 \\ \times\, 1.1 \\ \hline \end{array}$$
$$\begin{array}{r} 0.18 \\ \times\, 4.5 \\ \hline \end{array}$$
$$\begin{array}{r} 0.72 \\ \times\, 2.3 \\ \hline \end{array}$$
$$\begin{array}{r} 10.3 \\ \times\, 8.2 \\ \hline \end{array}$$

D

$$\begin{array}{r} 3.56 \\ \times\, 2.4 \\ \hline \end{array}$$
$$\begin{array}{r} 4.5 \\ \times\, 1.5 \\ \hline \end{array}$$
$$\begin{array}{r} 0.16 \\ \times\, 7.7 \\ \hline \end{array}$$
$$\begin{array}{r} 9.1 \\ \times\, 9.2 \\ \hline \end{array}$$
$$\begin{array}{r} 0.33 \\ \times\, 0.4 \\ \hline \end{array}$$

Solve. Round the answers to the nearest cent.

 E Bananas cost $0.69 per pound. What is the cost of 2.5 pounds of bananas?

 F Pears cost $1.25 per pound. What is the cost of 4.5 pounds of pears?

_____

_____

Fractions and Decimals • 5–6 © 2007 Creative Teaching Press

Name _____ Date _____

Zeros in the Product

Sometimes when you multiply decimals, you need to put one or more zeros in the product.

$$\begin{array}{r} 0.2 \\ \times\, 0.3 \\ \hline \end{array}$$
$$\begin{array}{r} 0.2 \\ \times\, 0.3 \\ \hline 6 \end{array}$$
$$\begin{array}{r} 0.2 \\ \times\, 0.3 \\ \hline 0.06 \end{array}$$
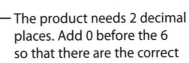 ← total of 2 decimal places

← The product needs 2 decimal places. Add 0 before the 6 so that there are the correct number of decimal places in the answer.

You can check your answers with fractions!

$$\frac{2}{10} \times \frac{3}{10} = \frac{6}{100} = 0.06$$

Multiply.

A
$$\begin{array}{r} 0.5 \\ \times\, 0.1 \\ \hline \end{array}$$
$$\begin{array}{r} 0.6 \\ \times\, 0.1 \\ \hline \end{array}$$
$$\begin{array}{r} 0.2 \\ \times\, 0.4 \\ \hline \end{array}$$
$$\begin{array}{r} 0.3 \\ \times\, 0.3 \\ \hline \end{array}$$
$$\begin{array}{r} 0.2 \\ \times\, 0.1 \\ \hline \end{array}$$

B
$$\begin{array}{r} 0.03 \\ \times\, 0.3 \\ \hline \end{array}$$
$$\begin{array}{r} 0.09 \\ \times\, 0.4 \\ \hline \end{array}$$
$$\begin{array}{r} 0.07 \\ \times\, 0.5 \\ \hline \end{array}$$
$$\begin{array}{r} 0.06 \\ \times\, 0.8 \\ \hline \end{array}$$
$$\begin{array}{r} 0.01 \\ \times\, 0.1 \\ \hline \end{array}$$

C
$$\begin{array}{r} 0.007 \\ \times\quad 2 \\ \hline \end{array}$$
$$\begin{array}{r} 0.003 \\ \times\quad 2 \\ \hline \end{array}$$
$$\begin{array}{r} 0.009 \\ \times\quad 8 \\ \hline \end{array}$$
$$\begin{array}{r} 0.004 \\ \times\quad 4 \\ \hline \end{array}$$
$$\begin{array}{r} 0.002 \\ \times\quad 2 \\ \hline \end{array}$$

D
$$\begin{array}{r} 0.24 \\ \times\, 0.3 \\ \hline \end{array}$$
$$\begin{array}{r} 0.32 \\ \times\, 0.2 \\ \hline \end{array}$$
$$\begin{array}{r} 0.016 \\ \times\quad 4 \\ \hline \end{array}$$
$$\begin{array}{r} 0.008 \\ \times\quad 7 \\ \hline \end{array}$$
$$\begin{array}{r} 0.024 \\ \times\quad 4 \\ \hline \end{array}$$

E
$$\begin{array}{r} 0.01 \\ \times\, 0.2 \\ \hline \end{array}$$
$$\begin{array}{r} 0.07 \\ \times\, 0.3 \\ \hline \end{array}$$
$$\begin{array}{r} 0.006 \\ \times\quad 9 \\ \hline \end{array}$$
$$\begin{array}{r} 0.23 \\ \times\, 0.3 \\ \hline \end{array}$$
$$\begin{array}{r} 0.26 \\ \times\, 0.3 \\ \hline \end{array}$$

Name _____ Date _____

Multiplying Multidigit Decimals

Multiply. Check that the number of decimal places in the product equals the number of decimal places in the factors.

 A
| 7.93 | 12.05 | 22.6 | 34.4 | 6.15 |
| × 6.2 | × 1.8 | × 0.14 | × 0.23 | × 4.5 |

B
| 62.3 | 2.8 | 9.01 | 1.37 | 114.5 |
| × 0.37 | × 5.6 | × 3.2 | × 2.8 | × 6.7 |

C
| 20.3 | 41.9 | 10.7 | 63.34 | 53.8 |
| × 46.2 | × 23.5 | × 53.6 | × 11.9 | × 2.06 |

Solve. Round each answer to the nearest tenth.

 D A bag of marbles weighs 15 pounds. What would 2.25 bags weigh?

 E A car is traveling 40.5 miles per hour. How far will it travel in 3.5 hours?

_____

_____

Fractions and Decimals • 5–6 © 2007 Creative Teaching Press

Dividing Decimals by Whole Numbers

To divide a decimal by a whole number, place a decimal point above the decimal point in the dividend. Then, divide as you would with whole numbers.

$$4\overline{)0.52} \longrightarrow 4\overline{)0.52} \longrightarrow \begin{array}{r} 0.13 \\ 4\overline{)0.52} \\ -4 \\ \hline 12 \\ -12 \\ \hline 0 \end{array}$$

Divide.

A $2\overline{)0.8}$ $3\overline{)0.9}$ $4\overline{)0.8}$ $6\overline{)0.6}$ $3\overline{)0.6}$

B $5\overline{)0.55}$ $2\overline{)0.48}$ $3\overline{)0.69}$ $8\overline{)0.96}$ $7\overline{)0.91}$

C $6\overline{)1.26}$ $9\overline{)8.46}$ $7\overline{)45.5}$ $3\overline{)7.47}$ $5\overline{)18.85}$

D $9\overline{)41.4}$ $5\overline{)31.5}$ $2\overline{)1.18}$ $6\overline{)9.24}$ $4\overline{)17.56}$

Solve.

E Jan had some string that was 9.42 meters long. She cut it into six equal pieces for a science project. How long was each piece?

F Mr. Lee has a board that is 6.45 feet long. He wants to cut it into three equal pieces. How long should each piece be?

_____

_____

Dividing Whole Numbers by Decimals

To divide a whole number by a decimal, follow these steps.

$$0.4\overline{)8}$$

1. Move the decimal point in the divisor to the right to make a whole number.

$$0.4\overline{)8.}$$

Move the decimal point 1 place to the right. (This is the same as multiplying by 10.)

Add a decimal point at the end of the dividend.

2. Move the decimal point in the dividend the same number of places. Add 0 as a placeholder.

$$4\overline{)8.0}$$

3. Divide.

$$\begin{array}{r} 20 \\ 4\overline{)80} \\ \underline{-8} \\ 00 \end{array}$$

Here's why it works:

$$0.4\overline{)8} = 8 \div 0.4 = \frac{8}{0.4} = \frac{8 \times 10}{0.4 \times 10} = \frac{80}{4} = 20$$

Rewrite each problem so that the divisor is a whole number. Then divide.

A $0.2\overline{)16}$ $0.4\overline{)24}$ $0.8\overline{)56}$ $0.3\overline{)36}$ $0.9\overline{)45}$

B $1.2\overline{)6}$ $1.3\overline{)39}$ $0.5\overline{)8}$ $0.7\overline{)49}$ $2.4\overline{)12}$

C $2.5\overline{)130}$ $0.5\overline{)7}$ $1.5\overline{)90}$ $3.6\overline{)72}$ $0.3\overline{)24}$

D $7.5\overline{)45}$ $2.3\overline{)92}$ $1.8\overline{)54}$ $2.6\overline{)13}$ $4.2\overline{)168}$

Fractions and Decimals • 5–6 © 2007 Creative Teaching Press

Name _____ Date _____

Dividing Decimals by Decimals

To divide a decimal by a decimal, follow these steps.
1. Move the decimal point in the divisor one or more places to the right to make a whole number.
2. Move the decimal point in the dividend the same number of places.
3. Put a decimal point in the quotient above the decimal point in the dividend.
4. Divide.

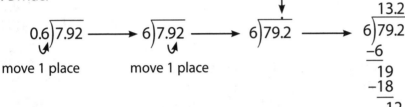

place decimal point here

$$
\begin{array}{r}
13.2 \\
6\overline{)79.2} \\
-6 \\
\hline
19 \\
-18 \\
\hline
12 \\
-12 \\
\hline
0
\end{array}
$$

Rewrite each problem so that the divisor is a whole number. Then divide.

A $0.4\overline{)2.8}$

B $0.6\overline{)3.6}$

C $0.3\overline{)8.4}$

D $0.05\overline{)2.5}$

E $0.9\overline{)83.7}$

F $0.7\overline{)5.18}$

G $0.03\overline{)0.234}$

H $0.4\overline{)4.36}$

I $0.02\overline{)0.54}$

J $1.6\overline{)0.352}$

K $2.4\overline{)0.768}$

L $0.13\overline{)0.624}$

Fractions and Decimals • 5–6 © 2007 Creative Teaching Press

Expressing Remainders as Decimals

Sometimes you get a remainder when you divide. You can express the remainder as a decimal. Simply add as many zeros as needed to the right of the dividend, and keep on dividing.

$$
\begin{array}{r} 9 \\ 4\overline{)37} \\ -36 \\ \hline 1 \end{array}
\longrightarrow
\begin{array}{r} 9. \\ 4\overline{)37.0} \\ -36\downarrow \\ \hline 10 \end{array}
\longrightarrow
\begin{array}{r} 9.2 \\ 4\overline{)37.0} \\ -36 \\ \hline 10 \\ -8 \\ \hline 2 \end{array}
\longrightarrow
\begin{array}{r} 9.25 \\ 4\overline{)37.00} \\ -36 \\ \hline 10 \\ -8 \\ \hline 20 \\ -20 \\ \hline 0 \end{array}
$$

remainder of 1

Place a decimal point to the right of the dividend and add a zero. Put another decimal point directly above it in the quotient. Bring down the 0 and divide. Repeat until you can no longer divide.

Divide. Express the remainders as decimals.

A $2\overline{)7}$ **B** $5\overline{)26}$ **C** $4\overline{)53}$ **D** $2\overline{)31}$ **E** $8\overline{)6}$

F $6\overline{)8.7}$ **G** $5\overline{)2.4}$ **H** $8\overline{)9.24}$ **I** $4\overline{)50.6}$ **J** $2\overline{)14.3}$

K $6\overline{)0.75}$ **L** $8\overline{)27}$ **M** $12\overline{)5.4}$ **N** $4\overline{)2.7}$ **O** $16\overline{)12.4}$

Fractions and Decimals • 5–6 © 2007 Creative Teaching Press

Multiplying by Powers of Ten

Watch what happens to the decimal point when you multiply by 10; 100; and 1,000.

$$0.347 \times 10 = 3.47$$

$$0.347 \times 100 = 34.7$$

$$0.347 \times 1,000 = 347. = 347$$

When you multiply a number by 10, the decimal point moves one place to the right.
When you multiply a number by 100, the decimal point moves two places to the right.
When you multiply a number by 1,000, the decimal point moves three places to the right.

Multiply.

A $10 \times 3.68 =$ _____ $100 \times 4.1 =$ _____ $10 \times 18.95 =$ _____

B $100 \times 6.435 =$ _____ $1,000 \times 3.9 =$ _____ $100 \times 8.01 =$ _____

C $2.57 \times 10 =$ _____ $16.305 \times 10 =$ _____ $7.513 \times 1,000 =$ _____

D $0.52 \times 10 =$ _____ $0.03 \times 100 =$ _____ $0.006 \times 100 =$ _____

E $1,000 \times 0.093 =$ _____ $10 \times 4.762 =$ _____ $0.07 \times 1,000 =$ _____

F $3.015 \times 100 =$ _____ $1,000 \times 0.058 =$ _____ $11.01 \times 10 =$ _____

Solve.

G What number times 0.76 gives a product of 76? _____

H What number times 0.014 gives a product of 0.14? _____

I What number times 1.008 gives a product of 1,008? _____

J What number times 3.027 gives a product of 302.7? _____

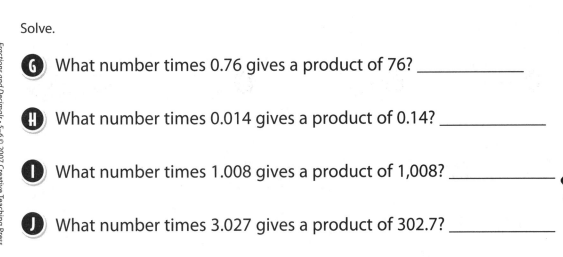

Fractions and Decimals • 5–6 © 2007 Creative Teaching Press

Dividing by Powers of Ten

Watch what happens to the decimal point when you divide by 10; 100; and 1,000.

$$3.47 \div 10 = 0.347$$
$$3.47 \div 100 = 0.0347$$
$$3.47 \div 1,000 = 0.00347$$

When you divide a number by 10, the decimal point moves one place to the left.
When you divide a number by 100, the decimal point moves two places to the left.
When you divide a number by 1,000, the decimal point moves three places to the left.

Divide.

A $65 \div 10 =$ _____ $24 \div 100 =$ _____ $29 \div 1,000 =$ _____

B $542 \div 1,000 =$ _____ $16.8 \div 10 =$ _____ $14.2 \div 100 =$ _____

C $17.89 \div 10 =$ _____ $9.4 \div 100 =$ _____ $326 \div 1,000 =$ _____

D $0.07 \div 10 =$ _____ $0.6 \div 100 =$ _____ $1.02 \div 10 =$ _____

E $0.56 \div 10 =$ _____ $4.7 \div 100 =$ _____ $125 \div 1,000 =$ _____

F $18 \div 10 =$ _____ $588 \div 1,000 =$ _____ $0.16 \div 10 =$ _____

Write $>$, $<$, or $=$ in the circles to compare the quotients.

G $3.1 \div 10$ ◯ $31 \div 100$ **H** $79 \div 1,000$ ◯ $7.9 \div 10$

I $112 \div 1,000$ ◯ $1.12 \div 10$ **J** $351 \div 1,000$ ◯ $35.1 \div 10$

K $4.7 \div 100$ ◯ $417 \div 1,000$ **L** $8 \div 100$ ◯ $0.08 \div 10$

M $6.2 \div 10$ ◯ $0.62 \div 10$ **N** $95.6 \div 100$ ◯ $956 \div 1,000$

Fractions and Decimals • 5–6 © 2007 Creative Teaching Press

Converting Fractions to Decimals Using Equivalent Fractions

Some fractions can be changed easily into decimals.

For a fraction with a denominator that is a multiple of 10, use the numerator to help you write the decimal.

If a fraction has a denominator that can be changed to a multiple of 10, change it. Then use the numerator to help you write the decimal.

$$\frac{7}{10}=0.7$$

$$\frac{35}{100}=0.35$$

$$\frac{619}{1,000}=0.619$$

$$\frac{1}{2}=\frac{5}{10}=0.5$$

$$\frac{3}{4}=\frac{75}{100}=0.75$$

$$\frac{4}{125}=\frac{32}{1,000}=0.032$$

Change the fractions to decimals.

A $\dfrac{9}{10}$ _____ $\dfrac{13}{100}$ _____ $\dfrac{765}{1,000}$ _____ $\dfrac{95}{100}$ _____

B $\dfrac{1}{2}$ _____ $\dfrac{1}{4}$ _____ $\dfrac{3}{4}$ _____ $\dfrac{19}{20}$ _____

C $\dfrac{43}{50}$ _____ $\dfrac{17}{25}$ _____ $\dfrac{316}{500}$ _____ $\dfrac{9}{125}$ _____

D $\dfrac{7}{10}$ _____ $\dfrac{241}{250}$ _____ $\dfrac{13}{20}$ _____ $\dfrac{37}{50}$ _____

E $\dfrac{4}{5}$ _____ $\dfrac{4}{100}$ _____ $\dfrac{7}{1,000}$ _____ $\dfrac{163}{250}$ _____

F $\dfrac{16}{25}$ _____ $\dfrac{499}{500}$ _____ $\dfrac{9}{20}$ _____ $\dfrac{18}{250}$ _____

Converting Fractions to Decimals Using Division

To change a fraction to a decimal, divide the numerator by the denominator.

$$\frac{5}{8} \longrightarrow 8\overline{)5} \longrightarrow \begin{array}{r} 0.625 \\ 8\overline{)5.000} \\ -48 \\ \hline 20 \\ -16 \\ \hline 40 \\ -40 \\ \hline 0 \end{array}$$

We're equal

$\frac{5}{8}$ 0.625

Use division to change the fractions to decimals.

A $\dfrac{3}{8}$

B $\dfrac{9}{12}$

C $\dfrac{3}{5}$

D $\dfrac{8}{32}$

E $\dfrac{24}{50}$

F $\dfrac{1}{8}$

G $\dfrac{6}{16}$

H $\dfrac{7}{8}$

I $\dfrac{11}{25}$

J $\dfrac{15}{24}$

K $\dfrac{3}{75}$

L $\dfrac{17}{20}$

M $\dfrac{45}{50}$

N $\dfrac{3}{12}$

O $\dfrac{12}{75}$

Fractions and Decimals • 5–6 © 2007 Creative Teaching Press

Name _____ Date _____

Review of Decimal Concepts

Write the matching fractions.

A 0.8 _____ 0.93 _____ 0.065 _____

B 0.004 _____ 0.05 _____ 0.021 _____

Compare the decimals. Write >, <, or = in the circles.

C 0.3 ◯ 0.09   0.15 ◯ 0.51   1.04 ◯ 1.040

D 7.16 ◯ 7.161   9.008 ◯ 9.080   5.071 ◯ 5.017

Write the numbers in order from the least to the greatest.

E
3.01	_____
3.11	_____
3.101	_____
3.011	_____

F
1.79	_____
1.7	_____
1.079	_____
1.09	_____

G
0.046	_____
0.6	_____
0.46	_____
0.064	_____

Round to the nearest tenth.

H 5.17 _____ 2.463 _____ 4.089 _____ 16.752 _____

Round to the nearest hundredth.

I 9.075 _____ 6.432 _____ 12.083 _____ 11.273 _____

Change the fractions to decimals.

J $\dfrac{13}{100}$ _____ $\dfrac{5}{20}$ _____ $\dfrac{64}{1,000}$ _____ $\dfrac{4}{25}$ _____

K $\dfrac{1}{8}$ _____ $\dfrac{21}{50}$ _____ $\dfrac{15}{24}$ _____ $\dfrac{3}{75}$ _____

Fractions and Decimals • 5–6 © 2007 Creative Teaching Press

Name _____ Date _____

Decimals–Addition and Subtraction Review

Solve.

A

| 9.31
+ 8.47 | 6.02
+ 0.99 | 12.832
− 9.5 | 10.08
+ 20.87 | 0.9
− 0.873 |

B

| 13.6
− 4.35 | 2.8
− 0.91 | 16.32
+ 15.84 | 24.821
− 16.05 | 30.4
− 17.23 |

C

| 48.76
+ 9.3 | 31.23
− 0.066 | 22.5
+ 14.97 | 61.302
− 59.08 | 50
− 18.7 |

D

| 12.3
− 4.56 | 8.901
+ 2.199 | 16.24
+ 9.8 | 57.8
− 24.004 | 41.27
− 16.085 |

E

| 0.08
0.935
+ 0.6 | 1.34
2.8
+ 5.999 | 6.358
0.9
+ 2.83 | 5.41
7.6
+ 8.3 | 9.217
0.008
+ 6.6 |

Fractions and Decimals • 5–6 © 2007 Creative Teaching Press